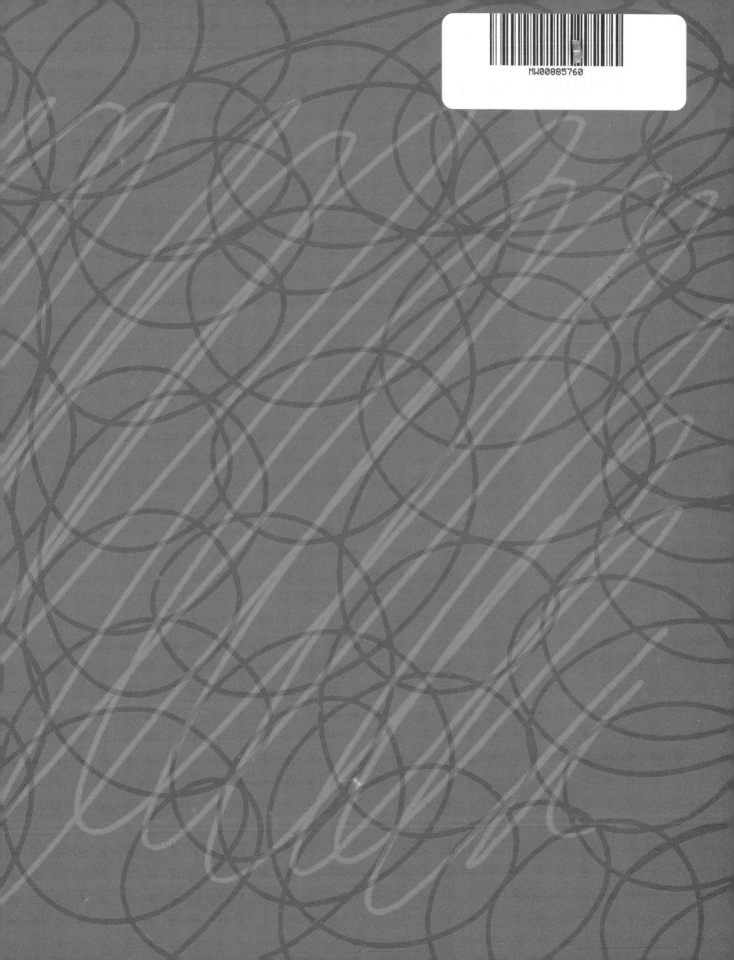

For Dr. Wendy —
I thank God
for the blessing
you are in
my life!

Romans 7
for kids

The Good That I Should

Written by Gwyn Borcherding
Pictures by Vincent Nguyen

Gwyn Borcherding

1 John 3:1

CONCORDIA PUBLISHING HOUSE • SAINT LOUIS

Romans 7:14-25

I do not understand what I do. For what I want to do I do not do, but what I hate I do. And if I do what I do not want to do, I agree that the law is good. As it is, it is no longer I myself who do it, but it is sin living in me. I know that nothing good lives in me, that is, in my sinful nature. For I have the desire to do what is good, but I cannot carry it out.

For what I do is not the good I want to do; no, the evil I do not want to do—this I keep on doing. ... When I want to do good, evil is right there with me.

For in my inner being I delight in God's law; but I see another law at work in the members of my body, waging war against the law of my mind and making me a prisoner of the law of sin at work within my members. ... Who will rescue me from this body of death? Thanks be to God—through Jesus Christ our Lord.

The good that I should do,
I often don't do.
The wrong that I shouldn't do,
that's what I do!

You know how it is
when your mom says, "Be good,
and do all the things
that you know that you should."

So you try hard to listen
and sit very still,
but one table over,
you see your friend Will.

He's making a face
and pointing at Drew,
Who is leaning way back
on his chair next to you.

Just a quick little nudge
of your toe on his chair,
and the next thing you know,
Drew is launched in the air.

He lands with a crash
and the class starts to giggle.
You know you're in trouble
and you nervously wiggle.

When we do something wrong,
God calls it a sin.
Who'll help us out of this mess
that we're in?

Thanks be to God
we have Jesus to win!
Forgiveness for us
and our whole load of sin.

The good that I should do,
I often don't do.
The wrong that I shouldn't do,
that's what I do!

You've heard it before, when
your dad says, "Don't fight."
And you glare at your sister,
'though you know it's not right.

Most times it's fun
when the two of you play,
But something she said
hurt your feelings today.

You know that it's best
if you obey your dad;
You really don't plan
to do anything bad.

But just then you reach out
and give her a shove.
Now what makes you mistreat
the sister you love?

So now you feel bad
and your sister is crying.
You're right back in trouble
without even trying!

When we do something wrong,
God calls it a sin.
Who'll help us out of this mess
that we're in?

Thanks be to God that
with Jesus there's grace
And there in His kingdom,
He's made us a place.

The good that I should do,
I often don't do.
The wrong that I shouldn't do,
that's what I do!

You've seen how it works
when your room is a mess,
But you want to go play
with your neighbor friend Jess.

It would make your mom's day
if you cleaned it before
She had to remind you
or tell you once more.

You could straighten up now
and get the job done.
But everyone else is outside
having fun.

You know Mom prefers
that you work and then play,
But you leave it and head out
the door anyway.

As you play with your friends,
in the back of your head,
You know you'd feel better if
you'd cleaned up instead.

When we don't do what's right,
God calls it a sin.
Who'll get us out of this mess
that we're in?

Thanks be to God
that He cleanses our heart.
We're baptized, forgiven!
We get a new start.

Sin makes us all struggle
to do the right thing.
But here's some good news
that will make your heart sing ...

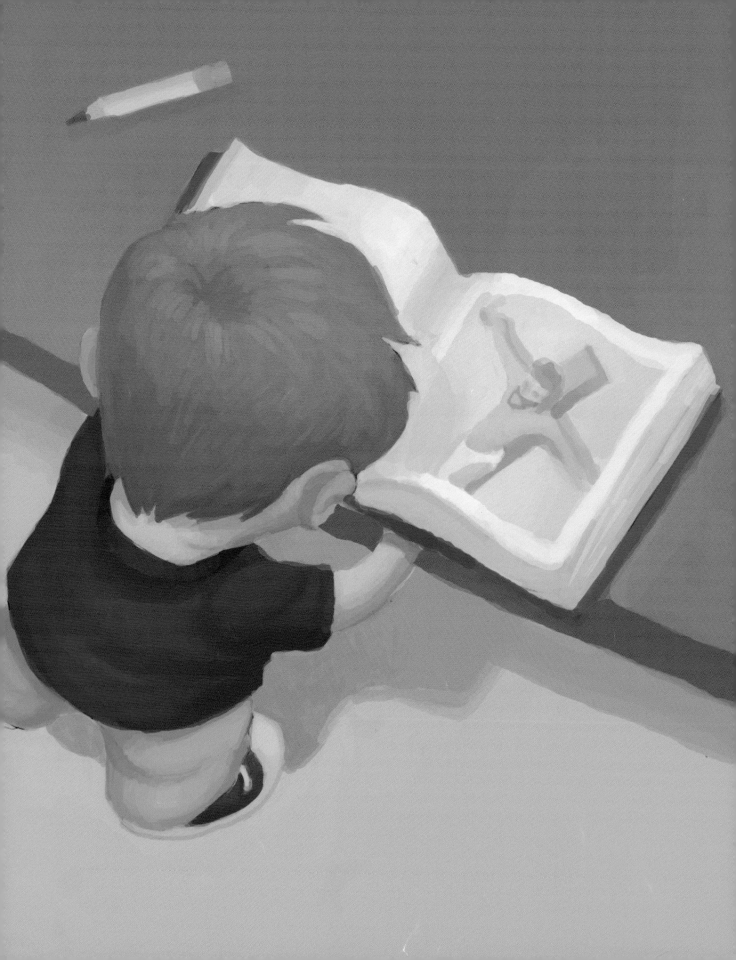

Although we all sin
and don't do as we should,
the Lord lived a life
that was perfectly good.

The punishment we deserved,
He took instead.
Repent. You're forgiven!
Believe what He said!

Jesus comes in His Word
and gives a fresh start.
We'll be His forever.
We never will part.

For good news you'll find
these words second to none:
God loves you so much
that He sent you His Son.

For
Micah and Kyle—
Who believe the Good News.

Text copyright © 2004 Gwyn Borcherding
Illustrations copyright © 2004 Vincent Nguyen
Published by Concordia Publishing House
3558 S. Jefferson Avenue
St. Louis, MO 63118-3968

The Scripture quotations in this publication are from the HOLY BIBLE: NEW INTERNATIONAL VERSION®.
Copyright © 1973, 1978, 1984 by the International Bible Society.
Used by permission of Zondervan Publishing House. All rights reserved.
Manufactured in the United States of America

1 2 3 4 5 6 7 8 9 10   13 12 11 10 09 08 07 06 05 04

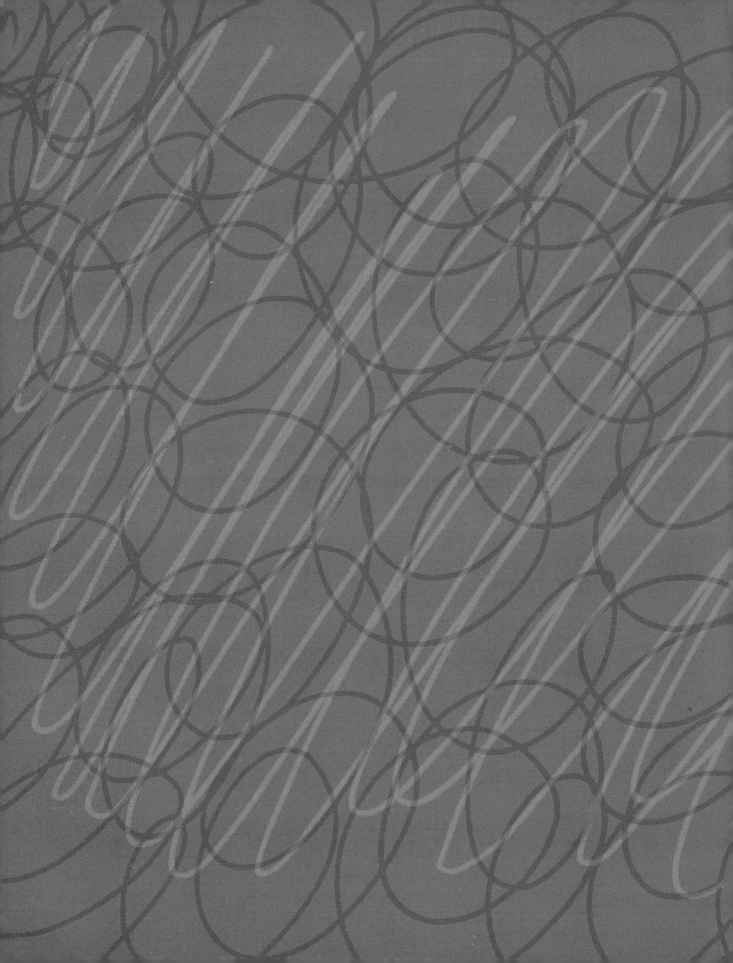